Dress-up Fashion

Things to Make and Do

Bath • New York • Singapore • Hong Kong • Cologne • Delhi
Melbourne • Amsterdam • Johannesburg • Auckland • Shenzhen

First published by Parragon in 2011

Parragon
Queen Street House
4 Queen Street
Bath BA1 1HE, UK

ISBN 978-1-4454-1807-0
Printed in China.

Contents

Getting Started

Tips for Success

Remember, everything in this book should be made with the supervision and help of a grown up! A step labeled with "Kids" means that a child can do this step on their own. Some items will need to be purchased from a supermarket or a craft/hobby store.

1 Prepare your space

Cover your work space with newspaper or a plastic or paper tablecloth. Make sure you are wearing clothes (including shoes!) that you don't mind becoming splattered with food, paint, or glue. But relax! You'll never completely avoid mess; in fact, it's part of the fun!

2 Wash your hands

Wash your hands before starting a new project, and clean up as you go along. Clean hands make for clean crafts! Remember to wash your hands afterwards too, using soap and warm water to remove any of the remaining materials.

3 Follow steps carefully

Follow each step carefully, and in the sequence in which it appears. We've tested all the projects; we know they work, and we want them to work for you, too.

4 Measure precisely

If a project gives you measurements, use your ruler, measuring cups, or measuring spoons to make sure you measure as accurately as you can. Sometimes, the success of the project may depend on it.

5 Be patient

You may need to wait while something bakes or leave paint, glue or clay to dry, sometimes for a few hours or even overnight. Be patient! Plan another activity while you wait, but it's important not to rush something as it may affect the outcome!

6 Clean up

When you've finished your project, clean up any mess. Store all the materials together so that they are ready for the next time you want to make and do. If you are making something with someone else then ensure it is a team effort!

Belle Rose Pin

Roses are very important to Belle. Breaking the spell on the enchanted rose meant that Belle could be with the Prince!

You will need

- A section cut from an egg carton
- Green paint
- Paintbrush
- Red felt 20 x 20 inches
- Safety scissors
- Glue and clear tape
- A safety pin

1 Cut off a single section from an egg carton. Cut the sides into points then paint it green to look like the bottom of a rose bud. Leave to dry.

2 Cut out ten circles from your red felt. These should have a diameter of 2¾ inches.

3 Roll up one of the felt circles. Stick some tape around one end. The felt should remain rolled up, but one end should be loose, forming the center of your rose.

Glue the remaining felt circles around this middle piece to form your rose. Tape a safety pin to the egg carton, then glue the rose inside.

Belle's tip:
You can pin this rose to a shirt, a coat, or even your bag. Beautiful!

Beautiful Fan

Jasmine loves living in such a hot place. But sometimes a Princess needs to cool down. This beautiful fan is perfect for hot weather or as a stylish accessory!

1

Draw three circles each 6 inches in diameter on the cardboard. You could use a small plate as a guide. Cut out the circles. Paint in your favorite colors. Paint one side at a time allowing each side to dry.

You will need

- Thick cardboard
- Small plate
- Glue
- Pencil
- Paint
- 2 ice-cream sticks
- Clear tape
- Ribbon
- Feathers and gems
- Glitter glue

2

Tape two wooden sticks together, then wind some ribbon around the outside. Secure the ribbon ends in place with a dot of glue or tape.

Kids

3

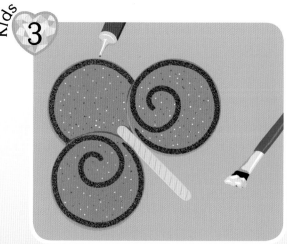

Glue the three circles together, arranging into a fan shape. Glue the stick into the middle. Using your glitter glue decorate the fan with a pretty pattern. Leave to dry.

4

Jasmine's tip:
You can paint your fan in your favorite colors. Match the fan with your favorite outfit!

Arrange feathers and gem on the fan. Glue feathers and gem to the fan when you are happy with the arrangement. Tie strips of ribbon to the bottom of the handle and stick another gem to the base where the ribbons join. Allow the glue to dry.

Tiana Celebration Mask

Tiana loves to wear a mask during Mardi Gras. You can make your own celebration mask for a special occasion or to put on your wall!

You will need

- Colored card stock
- Pencil
- Feathers of mixed colors
- Sequins
- Safety scissors
- Glue
- Glitter glue
- Elastic

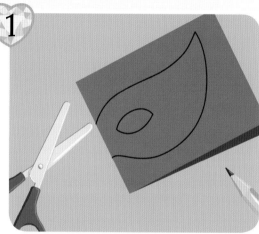

1

Fold a piece of 10 x 5 inches card stock in half. Draw half a mask shape. Make the eye hole around 1 inch from the folded edge. Cut out the mask outline and eye hole.

Kids 2

Decorate around the edge and eyes with glitter glue and allow to dry. Glue small sequins onto the mask to decorate. Leave to dry.

Kids 3

Turn the mask over and glue feathers along the top. Make sure they don't cover the eye holes. Allow to dry.

4

Make a small hole on each side of the mask. Thread a piece of elastic through each hole with a knot on the end. The knot should be tied on the reverse of the mask.

Tiana's tip:
You could make one of these for each of your friends, then take a picture of you all wearing them!

Flutter Butterfly Barettes

Aurora loves to see the butterflies flutter around. Create these nature inspired butterfly hair clips and see them flutter and sparkle in your hair!

1

Fold a piece of 4¾ x 4 inches paper in half. Draw half a butterfly shape along the fold, then cut it out.

You will need

- Card stock
- Colored paper
- Pencil
- Glitter
- Glue and safety scissors
- Sequins
- Pipe cleaner
- A plain hair barette

2

Thinly brush glue over the butterfly. Don't use too much or it will curl up. Sprinkle different colors of glitter over the glue.

3

Bend a piece of pipe cleaner down the middle of the butterfly for the body. Twist the ends together around the back.

4

Glue sequins for the eyes and spots, add thin strips of colored paper for the antennae. Glue the finished butterfly onto a plain hair barette. Allow to dry.

Aurora's tip:
Another idea you could try is decorating a head band. Try one butterfly on the side or stick a few across the top!

Castle Jewelry Stand

A castle is not just a castle, it is also a wonderful way to display your Princess fashion crafts and jewelry!

You will need

- A small cardboard box
- Cardboard tubes – different sizes
- A circular lid – for a balcony
- Colored card stock (dark blue) for doors and windows
- Pencil
- Safety scissors
- Glue
- Masking tape
- Small plates and a small jar
- Paints
- Brushes
- Sequins/gems

1 Arrange the tubes around a small box into a good castle shape. Cut the tubes if you need to so they vary in height. Don't glue them together yet.

2 Cut out some circles from card to make the turrets, they need to be around 5½ inches diameter for smaller turrets and 8 inches diameter for the bigger ones. Cut the circles in half so you have semi-circles.

3 Curl the semi circles into cone shapes and stick masking tape along the edge. Place each cone upside down into a small jar (to stop it rolling around) then glue the tube inside it.

4

Glue the turrets together around the box. To make a balcony, glue a lid to the largest turret, then stick a small turret on top. Let the glue dry, then paint your castle in a beige color to make it look like a castle wall.

5

When the paint has dried, glue the small windows and a door in place that you have cut out from the card stock. Glue sequins for extra sparkle. Then display your most precious jewelry from the turrets.

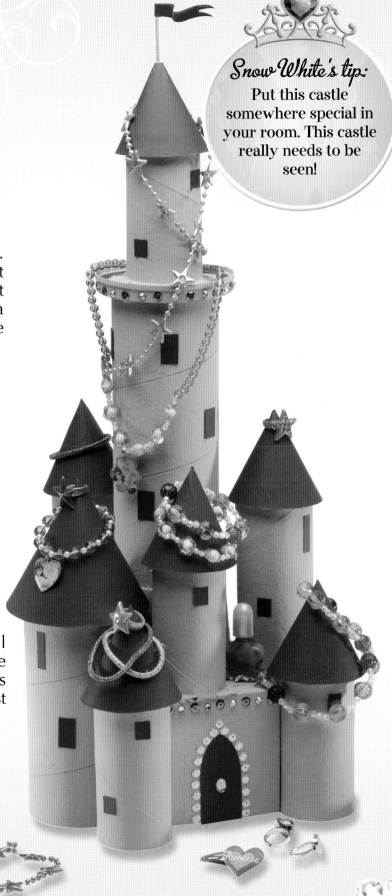

Snow White's tip:
Put this castle somewhere special in your room. This castle really needs to be seen!

Water Lily Apron

Tiana loves to cook! When you and someone special are baking wonderful treats together you'll both need an apron to protect your clothes.

Tape an ironed apron to a table with some card and newspaper underneath.

You will need

- A plain apron
- Masking tape
- A pencil
- Safety scissors
- Card stock
- Sponge
- Brushes
- Fabric paints

Draw a simple petal shape and also a lily pad shape onto card. Cut them out.

Sponge some white paint onto the petal shaped card stock, then press it down in the center of the apron. Repeat this until you have a flower, then allow to dry.

4

5

Sponge some pale green paint onto the card lily pad. Print it onto the apron, then flip it over to make another lily pad shape, then allow to dry.

Using a strip of card, dip one edge in green paint and create a printed pattern for the center of the flower. Then paint yellow dots to finish the flower.

Tiana's tip:
As a special touch why not write their name on their new apron!

Sparkly Star Charm

Cinderella loves the sparkle of a night sky filled with stars. Make this star charm and add some sparkle to your wardrobe.

You will need

- Salt dough recipe:

  2 cups plain flour
  1 cup of salt
  1 cup of water
  1 tablespoon of cooking oil

- A rolling pin
- Star shaped cookie cutters
- A toothpick
- Paint
- Brush
- Glue
- Gems
- A key chain or charm chain with a big jump ring (craft store)

1

Mix 2 cups of plain flour and 1 cup of salt in a mixing bowl. Add 1 cup of water, and 1 tablespoon oil. Mix together into a smooth dough. If your dough is too sticky, add more flour, if it is too crumbly add more water.

2

Knead the dough into a ball on a floured work surface. Roll it out to ½ inch thick. Cut out shapes using small cookie cutters.

3

Make a hole in the top of each shape with a toothpick or pencil. Be sure it goes all the way through and doesn't close up. Allow to dry. It could take a few days normally or only a few hours in an oven on a very low temperature.

Kids

4

Paint the shapes and leave to dry then glue on gems and glitter. Thread a jump ring through the holes and then attach onto a key chain.

Cinderella's tip:
You could make a heart charm, just cut out heart shapes instead of stars!

Jasmine

Dazzling Tiaras

To dazzle like a princess you need a wonderful tiara to wear. Follow these steps and create a colorful hair accessory.

You will need

- Card stock
- Cup
- White glue
- Tissue paper
- Curling ribbon
- Candy wrappers
- Pipe cleaners or string
- Tape
- Scissors

1 Cut a band of card stock 1 inch wide and long enough to fit around your head with 1½ inches extra at the back. Leave flat. Coat the headband with glue and cover with a layer of tissue paper.

2 Leave it to dry. Then trim the edges with scissors to make it neat. Tape the string or ribbon to the back of the headband at an angle. Spiral it around the headband and tape it at the other end.

3 Trace a small circle around a cup onto card. Cut it out. Lightly coat it with glue. Cover it with tissue paper and allow to dry. Trim the edges to make it neat.

4

Tape the circle face down on the center back of the headband so that half the circle shows from the front. Now you are ready to decorate your tiara with gold hearts and a scrunched up candy wrapper.

5

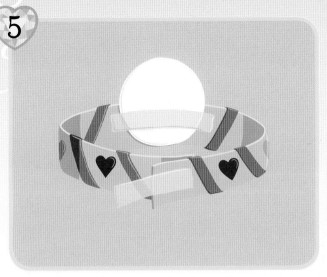

Ask someone to help you hold the band in place around your head and tape it together at the right size. Then take it off and tape the ends.

Jasmine's tip:
Here are some ideas for other tiaras you could try making.

Tiana Pretty Necklace

Now let's make a pretty with Tiana.
You can use these shapes and colors,
or choose your own.

Kids

1

Paint the elbows in a pink princess color and leave to dry on top of toothpicks stuck into modeling clay. If you want, as an added option, you can add a coating of glue and glitter and allow to dry.

You will need

- Dried pasta shapes:
  30 elbows
- Acrylic paints: pastel pink
- Glitter and glue
- Lump of modeling clay
- Toothpicks
- Colored string, elastic, or cord
- Button

2

Tie a button to the string while you thread the shapes to keep them from falling off!

Thread each elbow onto the colored string or cord. Repeat this until all the pasta is threaded.

Knot the two ends of the string together, making sure you have made your necklace big enough to go over your head.

Tiana's tip:
There are a lot of different pasta shapes, like twirls or bow ties. Try a different style like in the picture!

Ariel Ocean Bracelet

Ariel is always so inspired by the ocean world. These beads are beautiful ocean blues, green, and yellows!

1

Roll the three colors of clay into sausage shapes and put them side by side. Using a plastic knife, cut sections of about the same size through all three lengths together.

You will need

- Air-drying clay: green, yellow, turquoise
- Plastic knife
- 15 toothpicks
- Mug or glass
- Darning needle
- Thin elastic thread
- Safety scissors

2

Take a section and roll it into a ball between your palms until the colors are swirled together. Repeat until you have made about 15 balls.

Kids

3

4

Gently push a toothpick through the middle of each ball. Balance the sticks across the top of a mug or glass, so that the beads are fully exposed to the air, and allow them to dry. They will be ready in about 24 hours.

Using a darning needle, thread the beads onto thin elastic until you have enough to go around your wrist comfortably. Tie the two ends of elastic together and trim the ends.

Ariel's tip:
The ocean shimmers with all the colors of the rainbow, so you can make these beads in any color you like!

Royal Crown

Aurora wears her royal crown with pride. This crown is fit for a royal princess! You can be the ruler of your own princess kingdom!

You will need

- Tracing paper and pencil
- Strip of gold cardboard 5 x 24 inches
- Scissors, white glue and brush
- Holographic film
- 2 strips of gold cardboard: 1½ x 13 inches
- Paperclips and paper fastener
- Purple felt
- Dinner plate
- Strips of cotton wool
- Black acrylic paint and fine brush
- Assorted colored gems

1

Trace a crown shape onto tracing paper. Transfer it onto the back of the gold cardboard, then repeat, putting the second section up to the first. Cut out the whole strip.

2

3

Push a paper fastener through where the strips meet.

Glue the holographic foil along the base, then glue gems along the top. Glue the two ends together so the crown fits loosely on your head. Hold in place with paperclips. Let dry.

Mark halfway between the shapes with the pencil. Glue the gold strips to the inside of the band where these marks are. Hold in place with paperclips. Let dry.

4

Trace around the dinner plate and cut out a circle of purple felt. Make small snips all around the outside of the felt circle. Attach the felt to the inner brim, gluing bit by bit along the clipped edge. Let dry.

5

Cut a strip of cotton wool about 2 inches wide. Glue it along the bottom edge of the crown. Paint black spots about 1 inch apart along the length of the cotton wool.

Aurora's tip:
Crown's are not only gold, but silver, pink, or any pretty color you like!

Friendship Bands

We all know Snow White has seven best friends! Show your best friend how much you care with this great friendship band in pretty princess colors.

You will need

- 4 strands of cotton thread: 2 mauve, 1 pink, and 1 purple (or the colors of your choice), each 20 inches long
- 1 large bead
- 4 medium-sized beads

Take the 4 strands of cotton thread and tie them together, 8 inches from one end.

Thread the large bead on the bracelet and push it up as far as the knot.

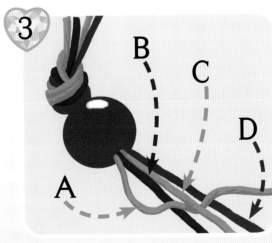

Spread out the 4 strands so that the 2 mauve strands are first and third from the left. Weave A over B, under C and over D. Pull A gently to tighten.

4

Continue weaving B over C, under D and over A, working over, under, over. Pull gently to tighten before starting on the next left-hand strand.

5

Continue weaving until you are about 3 inches from the end, then tie the knotted strands into a knot, leaving the ends loose.

6

Thread a medium-sized bead onto each of the four loose strands and tie a knot to keep it in place.

Snow White's tip:
Give this band as a birthday present! Who would you give your band to?

Flower Garland

Make this beautiful flower necklace.
Be inspired by the colors in nature.

You will need

- 80 sheets of tissue paper in 2 different colors (40 of each) cut into squares of 8 x 8 inches
- Bag of pipe cleaners
- Elastic or ribbon
- Safety scissors

Kids **1**

Stack four sheets of one color tissue paper together and fold over five times to make an accordion shape.

2

Cut both ends into a round shape then twist a pipe cleaner around the middle. Don't trim the ends of the pipe cleaner.

Kids **3**

Gently separate out the tissue paper on both sides of the pipe cleaner into a flower shape.

4

Twist the ends of the pipe cleaner around the ribbon or elastic and make sure the ends are not sticking out. Keep adding, alternating colors, flowers until your garland is done.

Snow White's tip:
What's your favorite flower? Use it as inspiration for your garland!

Cinderella *Glitter Slippers*

With help from the Fairy Godmother, Cinderella sparkled at the royal ball in her slippers. Now you can too, with these pretty glitter slippers!

Kids 1

Glue the gems to the slipper and allow to dry.

Cinderella's tip:
You don't just have to try dots, you could draw flowers or hearts, or even write your name on your shoes!

Kids 2

Next, add some more detail using the glitter glue. Gently make glittery dots on your shoes around the gems. Do one color at a time and let dry before applying more.